Sarah Lindsay

About this book

Preparation for school

- Your child will be following the Primary National Strategy in school.
- This book follows the same content as the Primary National Strategy, and will give your child helpful preparation and practice in punctuation.

Using the book

- Each double page spread has a common thematic context, i.e. cats, river rescue, etc.
- Each page is then divided into three sections.
  Learn about: An initial introduction to the subject.
  Now try these: A chance to do further work on the subject.
  Challenge: A more challenging exercise that pulls together the skills introduced in the sections above.

Helping your child

- Always talk through the work on the page to make sure your child understands what he or she is working on.
- Don't do too much in one sitting. One double page spread is probably enough at a time for a child's concentration span.
- At the end of each spread you can reward your child by sticking a gold star in the box.
- Most importantly, give plenty of praise and encouragement. Learning always works best when based on success, fun and enjoyment!

PERMISSIONS
pp.20-21 Roald Dahl
From: *What's Their Story*
Roald Dahl   Andrea Shavick
pp. 4-7
(approx. 270 words)
Oxford University Press

OXFORD
UNIVERSITY PRESS

Great Clarendon Street, Oxford OX2 6DP

Oxford University Press is a department of the University of Oxford.
Oxford is a registered trade mark of Oxford University Press
in the UK and in certain other countries

Author Sarah Lindsay
Cover illustration by Charlie Fowkes
Inside illustrations by Bill Bolton

First published in 2009

British Library Cataloguing in Publication Data

Data available

ISBN: 978-0-19-838734-3
2 4 6 8 10 9 7 5 3 1

Printed in China

Paper used in the production of this book is a natural,
recyclable product made from wood grown in sustainable forests.
The manufacturing process conforms to the environmental
regulations of the country of origin.

CONTENTS

Seaside fun

Learn about

If we didn't use sentences in our writing, it would be hard to understand what has been written.
Sentences start with a capital letter and end with a full stop.

Underline the sentences that are written correctly.

It is the beginning of the holidays.
when we get there
We are nearly there
We are going to the seaside.
I can't wait to build a sandcastle.

Now try these

Sentences can ask a question, be an instruction or make a point.

What time is it?

Pick up your spade!

The sun is hot.

Write two of your own sentences about a visit to the seaside.

1. ....

2. ....

Challenge

It is hard to make sense of the passage below.
Copy the passage adding the missing capital letters and full stops.

we arrived at the beach very early in the morning mum and Dad wanted to get the best spot we were having such fun that we didn't notice the tide coming in until our towels were all wet maybe Mum and Dad hadn't chosen the best spot after all

....

....

....

....

Seaside fun

Learn about

A sentence makes complete sense.
Nothing else needs to be added for it to be understood.

Underline the complete sentences below.

Dad bought us an ice lolly each.
It made us.
Holly dropped hers on.
She cried as her ice lolly melted.
Dad went and bought.
At last Holly was smiling again.

Now try these

Look at the sentences you didn't underline in the 'Learn about' section above.
There should be 3 of them.

Make them into complete sentences using your own words.

....

....

....

Challenge

A sentence usually has at least one noun and one verb.

noun = naming word

verb = doing or being word

Underline the nouns and circle the verbs in each of these sentences.

A dog knocked over our sandcastle.
Ben caught a jellyfish in a rock pool.
We buried Dad in the sand.
We walked home.

Letters

Learn about

We already know **capital letters** are used at the beginning of sentences. Did you know the word **I** is always written as a capital letter?

Copy these sentences adding the missing capital letters.

the sun was shining as i woke this morning.

....

it is time i had my breakfast.

....

Now try these

Capital letters are also used for people's names and titles.

Abhaya Singh   Sir Alexander Fleming

Write four people's names, including their surnames.
Can you include a name with a title?

....

....

Challenge

Places need **capital letters**. These include house names, road names, towns and countries e.g. Tetbury Road.

Rewrite this address correctly.

mr james jackman
sunnymead house
32 charlton road
edinburgh
scotland
EL24 9DR

Letters

Learn about

Capital letters make words easier to read and understand. The main words in titles of books, songs, poems, films and plays begin with capital letters.
e.g. Harry Potter and the Philosopher's Stone.

Read these sentences carefully and rewrite the titles that need capital letters.

I love the book charlotte's web.

....

Can we see cinderella at the cinema?

....

Now try these

Days of the week, months and special days all need capital letters too.

Add the missing capital letters to each of these words.

.... onday	.... uly	.... hristmas	.... riday
.... eptember	.... ay	.... iwali	.... ctober

Challenge

This is part of a letter.
Rewrite it adding the missing capital letters.

dear ali,
we are having a great time in australia. on tuesday we went to the beach. on friday we are going to the sydney opera house to see joseph's dreamcoat. jake is scared by the spiders. i am being brave!

....

....

....

....

....

....

Why?

Learn about

This is a **question mark ?**.
When a sentence asks a question it must end with a ?.
Finish these sentences with a full stop or a question mark.

What is the time ....
Where are my pyjamas ....
Let's go and play ....
Why is it raining ....

Now try these

Questions can begin with many words.
Why is a word that can be used at the beginning of a question.

Write five more words that begin with **w** that might start questions.

Challenge

Hannah is thinking of an animal.
Guy can ask four questions before he has to guess what the animal might be.
Write four questions Guy might ask.

Why?

Learn about

Look carefully at the **question mark**.
Can you see the **full stop** in the question mark?
A question mark is used instead of a full stop.

Copy the sentences.
Remember to start with a capital letter and end with a question mark.

why do I have to tidy my room ....

what shall I wear today ....

Now try these

Write a question about each of these sentences.
Begin each question with a different word.

We have run out of milk. Why have we run out of milk?

I made some milkshakes. ....

The milkshakes used two cartons of milk. ....

I made chocolate milkshake. ....

Challenge

Add the missing **full stops** and **question marks** to this short passage.

"Why do I have to go shopping ..... " Kyle asked, "Can't I go to Sam's house instead ..... "
His Mum replied, "I'm afraid not as Sam's Mum has to go shopping as well ..... "
"Would you like to meet them for a pizza later ..... "
"Yes, can we ..... " said Kyle excitedly .....

Fire!

Learn about

This is an **exclamation mark !**.
When a sentence or phrase wants to stress a special meaning it must end with an !.

Finish these sentences with a question mark or exclamation mark.

Can I smell smoke ....
Quick, grab some water ....
Look at that fire ....
Who started the fire ....

Now try these

Exclamation marks can show surprise, anger, joy, pain, danger, orders, humour etc.

Using a line, match these exclamations with the four words.

surprise	Don't ever do that again!
anger	That hurts!
joy	What a surprise!
pain	I love it!
	I don't believe it!
	How dare you!
	Ouch!
	What great news!

Challenge

Look at the picture carefully. Fill in the speech bubbles with a sentence or phrase that needs an **exclamation mark**.

Fire!

Learn about

Look carefully at the **exclamation mark**.
Can you see the full stop in the exclamation mark?
An exclamation mark is used instead of a full stop.

Copy the sentences.
Remember to start with a capital letter.
End with an exclamation mark or a full stop.

watch out, the bath will overflow

....

i think you are wasting water

....

Now try these

Show each of these feelings or actions by writing a sentence or phrase using an **exclamation mark**.

fear = Help! I'm going to fall!

danger ....

excitement ....

greeting ....

Challenge

You shouldn't use more than one ! at a time.

Rewrite this passage using the **exclamation marks** correctly.

Dear Ben,
We are having a great time!!
Yesterday we had a fire on the beach!
It was brilliant!!!! Then it rained!!
When you visit we will build a fire
with you too!
Love Kyle

....

....

....

....

....

At the shops

Learn about

Commas are useful. They make it clear where words are part of a list. The last word in a list is usually separated with 'and' instead of a comma.

Sam bought a pen, pencil, ruler **and** rubber with her money.

Add the missing commas to these sentences.

The shopkeeper stacked tomatoes cucumbers onions and radishes.
Mum bought kebabs steaks and burgers for the BBQ.

Now try these

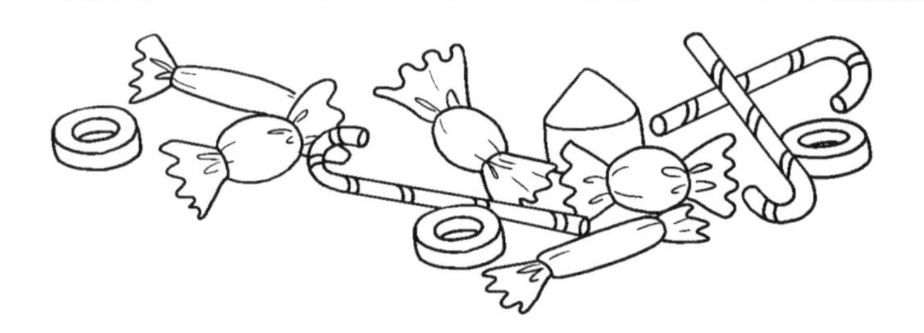

Write three sentences each listing items you might buy in a shop.
Don't forget the commas!

....

....

....

Challenge

Sometimes we need commas between groups of words.

Kyle was asked to buy [group: a bunch of grapes], [group: five bananas], [group: a selection of plums] **and** [group: a pineapple].

Carefully add the missing commas to these lists.

Hannah needs a pair of jeans a purple T-shirt two pairs of socks and new shoes.
We need some dog food a dog lead a few toys and a bed for our new puppy.
I could eat a bag of crisps some pizza slices and a chocolate bar for a snack!

At the shops

▼ Learn about

As well as separating nouns, commas can separate adjectives or verbs.

adjective = describing word

noun = naming word

verb = doing or being word

Copy these sentences adding the missing commas.

The scruffy long-haired muddy dog stole sweets from the shop.

....

The shopkeeper screamed yelled ran and pounced on the dog.

....

▼ Now try these

Add the missing commas to this passage. There are 8 missing commas.

On Friday Mum took me shopping for a pair of shiny new blue shoes. In the first shoe shop we were greeted by a grumpy tired assistant who prodded yanked and squeezed my feet until they hurt. We left that shop as soon as we could. The next shop sold boots flip-flops trainers and slippers but no shoes. Finally we bought some shoes. I came home with a pair of shiny new red shoes!

▼ Challenge

Write three sentences. The first must include a list with four nouns, the second a list with four adjectives and the third a list with three verbs.

1. ....

2. ....

3. ....

What is happening?

Learn about

Read the words in the speech bubbles.

What was said first? ....

Who was going to try to score a goal? ....

What do you think the neighbour wants to say? ....

Now try these

Write in the speech bubbles what might be being said in this picture.

Challenge

" " or ' ' are called speech marks. They show the words people speak.

"Let's sit under the tree," suggested Aimee.

Put the missing speech marks in these sentences.

I love having a picnic, said Bola.
Me too, replied Aimee.
We should eat quickly as I think it might rain! muttered Ellie.

What is happening?

Learn about

When someone starts to speak it must always begin with a **capital letter**.

Tick the sentences that have been written correctly.

"Grandad, can we go to the Water Park tomorrow?" asked Helen. ....
"yes if you go to bed early tonight," he replied. ....
"shall we take a picnic?" said Helen thoughtfully. ....
"What a good idea," muttered Grandad. ....

Now try these

Write in what Grandad and Helen are saying to each other.

Challenge

Now write each speech bubble from the cartoon above into a sentence. Remember to use **speech marks**.

Picture 1. ....

Picture 2. ....

Picture 3. ....

Cats

Learn about

Commas are used when a short pause is needed in a sentence.

The kittens, who were very hungry, gobbled up all their food.

Add the missing commas to these sentences.

Barney our little black dog watched the kittens from his bed. Then to Barney's surprise they started to eat his food!

Now try these

Copy the sentences adding the missing full stops and commas.

Our cat Tilly who loves catching mice usually brings them into the house

....

Cleo an old cat spends most of the day asleep on the sofa

....

George a stray cat often eats left-over food from restaurants

....

Challenge

Complete each of these sentences.

Our cat, ...

The pretty kittens, ...

The cat who lives next door, ...

Cats

Learn about

If a sentence is long, adding a comma will make it easier to read. Commas can separate clauses. A clause is a part of a sentence with a verb.

Underline the two clauses in each of these sentences, the first clause is underlined for you.

The lions pounced on their prey, killing the antelope quickly.
The lions relax in the shade of a tree, flies buzzing around them.

Now try these

Add the missing commas to this passage.

The Golding Family were going on a day safari. They excitedly packed their camera and binoculars at the last minute remembering the suncream. They were going to an animal watering hole an uncomfortable and slow ride away on an unmade road. Eventually they got there tired and sore. Suddenly their discomfort was forgotten as a cheetah and her cub slowly wandered to the water for a drink. Before long a group of lions had joined them the young ones playing at the water's edge. On the return journey while bouncing in the back of the truck the Golding Family talked about their exciting day.

Challenge

Write three sentences, each with a comma showing where a short pause is needed.

1. ....

2. ....

3. ....

Haircut hassle

Learn about

Sometimes two words are put together to make one word and a letter, or letters, is squeezed out.

did not = didn't

The **apostrophe '** shows where the letter '**o**' has been squeezed out.

I didn't want blue hair!

Join these words together in the same way.

do not = ... was not = ... could not = ... is not = ...

Now try these

When two words are joined together it is called a **contraction**.

Using a line, match these contractions with the two words they are made from.

haven't	they will
they're	I have
I'll	she will
they'll	have not
I've	I will
she'll	they are

Challenge

Write the two words each of these **contractions** are made from.

You're going to have to go back to the hairdressers!

didn't = ... we've = ...

he'll = ... we're = ...

they've = ... you're = ...

Haircut hassle

Learn about

Look how some contractions are made using pronouns.
Circle the pronoun in each of these pairs, then write the contraction.

we have = ...

she will = ...

we will = ...

they are = ...

he is = ...

I have = ...

Now try these

There are some strange contractions. With a line, match these words with their contraction. Watch out, one contraction matches with two word sets!

I would	shan't
will not	o'clock
of the clock	I'd
I had	won't
shall not	

Challenge

When to use it's or its can be confusing.
If it is or it has fits into the sentence use it's.

It's made its home in your messy hair!

Correctly add it's or its to these sentences.

'............ time you had your hair cut!'

'But .... always been like this and you haven't worried.'

'True, but now a spider has made .... home in your hair.'

'Ahhh .... not true!'

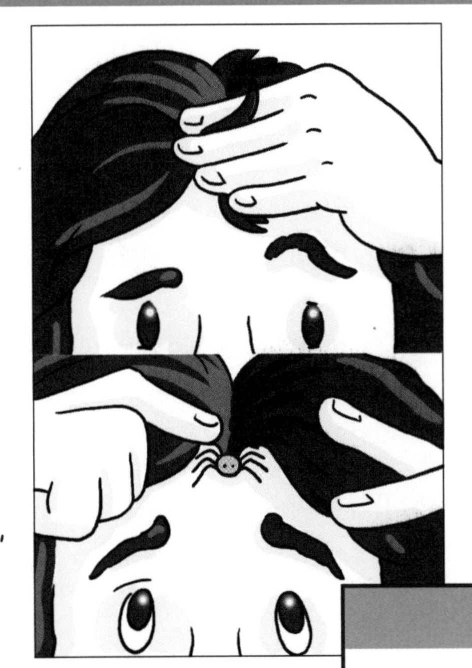

Roald Dahl

Paragraphs split long pieces of writing into smaller sections that make it easier to understand. Each paragraph has sentences about a similar topic, the next paragraph then moves the writing on to the next bit of information.

Look carefully at how the paragraphs are laid out in this piece of writing about Roald Dahl.

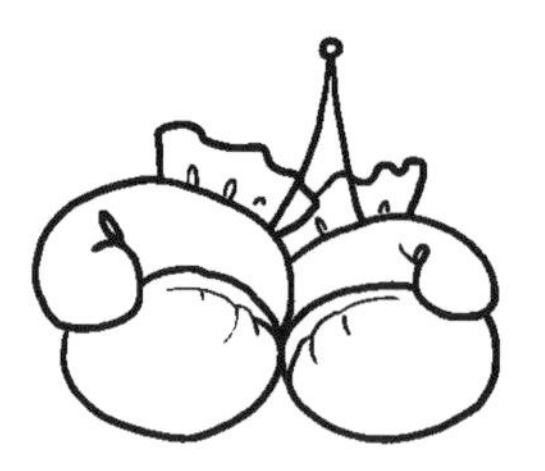

Today Roald Dahl is known as a famous children's author. But during his life he was also a boxing champion and a fighter pilot, and he invented a machine that saved thousands of children's lives.

Roald was born in 1916 in Cardiff, Wales. He lived with his Norwegian parents, one brother and four sisters in a grand house with acres of farmland. Every summer the whole family travelled to Norway to visit Roald's grandparents. While the rest of the family went out in their boat, Roald sat on his grandmother's lap, listening to her wonderful stories about witches and giants and magic. He was spellbound.

When Roald was only three years old, two very sad events happened. His sister Astri became very ill and died. Then three weeks later, his father also died. Little Roald felt terribly sad and lonely.

By the age of six, Roald was already a bit of a daredevil. Instead of simply walking to school, he liked to hurtle along on a tricycle right down the middle of the road!

He was always up to mischief. One day he decided to play a trick on the owner of the local sweet shop. All the children called her a witch because she had long dirty fingernails and a cross, witch's voice. While his friends kept her busy, Roald slipped a dead mouse into one of her jars of sweets. But somehow she discovered who had played the trick and told his headmaster. Roald's punishment was a terrible beating. When his mother saw the bruises she vowed never to send him back to that school again.

Roald Dahl by Andrea Shavick

Roald Dahl

Learn about

Each time a new **paragraph** begins the first line is moved in slightly (indented) to make it easier to see the start of the paragraph.

Write the first two words of each paragraph about Roald Dahl on page 20.

Paragraph 1. Today Roald

Paragraph 2. ....

Paragraph 3. ....

Paragraph 4. ....

Paragraph 5. ....

Now try these

Each **paragraph** is a unit of writing.
Write a short summary of each paragraph.

Paragraph 1. A general summary of Roald Dahl's achievements.

Paragraph 2. ....

Paragraph 3. ....

Paragraph 4. ....

Paragraph 5. ....

Challenge

Write a final **paragraph** to finish the writing about Roald Dahl. It needs to sum up Roald Dahl's early life. Don't forget to indent your paragraph!

....

....

....

River rescue

▼ Learn about

Remember, " " or ' ' are called speech marks.
They show the words people speak.

Put the missing speech marks in these sentences.
The comma must go inside the speech marks.

Let's go down to the river today, said Ben.
Good idea, we could take a picnic, replied Aziz.
I'll meet you in half an hour, called Ben as he dashed off to get ready.

▼ Now try these

As well as the speech marks, a comma is put at the end of the words actually spoken.
Remember, the comma must go inside the speech marks.

"Look at the river," said Aziz.

Put the missing speech marks and commas in these sentences.

Look at the boat said Ben.
He's waving to us giggled Aziz.
I think he needs help said Ben concerned.

▼ Challenge

Write out the conversation in the speech bubbles using speech marks and commas.

River rescue

Learn about

If the person speaking is asking a question, instead of the comma a question mark is added inside the speech marks.

"Who shall I call?" asked Aziz. "I've got my phone."

Add a comma or question mark to each of these sentences.

"I think we should call the fire brigade......" replied Ben.
"Look, there's a rope," said Aziz. Shall we try and throw it to him......"

Now try these

Write these sentences correctly.
Add the missing punctuation.

Can you catch this rope called Aziz.

....

Try again I missed it shouted the man.

....

OK let's try one more time said Ben.

....

I've caught it at last laughed the man.

....

Challenge

Copy the sentences. Add the missing punctuation.

Hang on a minute while we tie the rope to this tree called the boys.

....

Can you pull yourself in now Ben shouted.

....

Yes I can the man replied. Thank you so much.

....

Playtime

▼ Learn about

Remember, sentences can end in a **full stop** (.), **question mark** (?) or **exclamation mark** (!).

Look carefully at these sentences.
Mark them with a tick if they are correct and a cross if incorrect.

Shall we play football. ....
I want to read quietly. ....
Let's make two mixed teams! ....
Can I play too? ....
Great goal! ....
Fantastic. ....

▼ Now try these

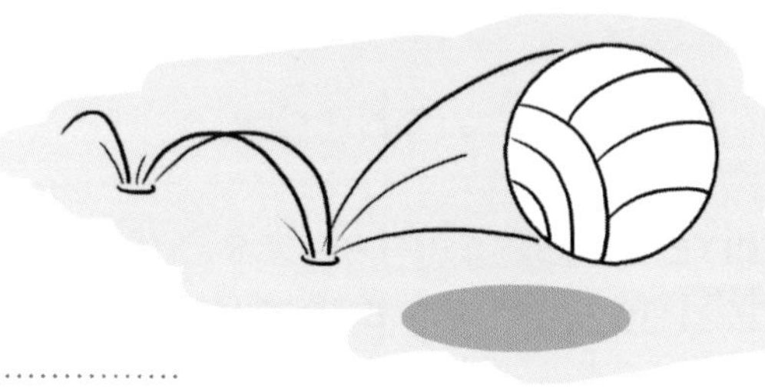

Write correctly the sentences you marked with a cross.

....

....

....

▼ Challenge

Write two sentences ending with full stops about a playtime you have enjoyed.

....

....

Think about the next playtime you will have. Write two questions about it.

....

....

Playtime

Learn about

Add the missing punctuation at the end of each sentence.

Shall we play tag at playtime.......
I'll ask Nathan and Fran to play too ....
Quick, hurry up.......

That's a good idea ....
That's the bell, time for playtime ....
Where are the others.......

Now try these

Look at the picture. Write three sentences about it, one ending with a **full stop**, one with a **question mark** and one with an **exclamation mark**.

....

....

....

Challenge

Add the missing punctuation marks to this passage.
Then add two or three more sentences, continuing the story.

Mrs Singh asked her class if they would like an extra playtime.......
"Yes......." they all cheered.......
"It is a reward for the excellent work you have done this afternoon," she explained
"How about 10 minutes on the field......."
The class ran out chatting and calling to each other.......

....

....

....

Belonging

Learn about

Apostrophes are also used to show when something belongs to someone.

If the name or noun is in the singular, use 's.

the boy's football boots

The football boots belong to the boy.

Add the missing apostrophes.

the dogs bowl
the childs homework
the birds nest
the mans jumper
Queen Elizabeths crown
the lions tail

Now try these

Read these sentences carefully.
Add the missing apostrophes.

Niall tore the books page by accident.

We were driving along when the cars tyre suddenly went flat.

The plants flower drooped in the sun.

Mrs Thompsons cat was rushed to the vet after having an accident.

Challenge

Write three sentences of your own, each with an apostrophe that shows when something belongs to someone.

....

....

....

Belonging

Learn about

If the name or noun is in the plural and ends in s, use s'.

the ants' nest

The nest that belongs to the ants.

Add the missing apostrophes.

the players shirts
the dancers shoes
the swans nests
the shops sales
the girls hats
the lorries drivers

Now try these

Rewrite these phrases adding an **apostrophe**, like this:

the books of the teachers .... the teachers' books

the surgeries of the doctors ....

the nests of the birds ....

the paws of the dogs ....

the flowers of the gardeners ....

Challenge

Add the missing **apostrophes** to these sentences.
Watch out, some will need 's and some s'!

The wind and rain plucked the roses petals from the bush.
Lord Buckleys horse sprinted across the field.
The crows squawking woke the campers early in the morning.
Many singers voices could be heard as the music began.

A school visit

Learn about

What do you remember about capital letters?

Class 3 are going on a school visit to a wildlife park.
Copy and write correctly the words that need capital letters.

wildlife park	tuesday	coach	mrs griffiths
giraffe	packed lunch	primary school	june

....

Now try these

Add the missing commas in these sentences.

I must remember my packed lunch a coat in case it rains some money and a pen.
Class 3 the noisiest class in the school waited impatiently for the coach.
At last the coach a big and smart one arrived and we set off.

Challenge

Write three sentences showing a conversation between two children on their way to the wildlife park.
Don't forget the speech marks and commas!

....

....

....

....

....

....

A school visit

Learn about

Complete each of these sentences with the correct punctuation mark.

The class arrived at the wildlife park and gathered around their teacher ....
At last we are here .... Wow, look over there .... Is it a tiger or a leopard.......
Class 3 was split into three groups and given clipboards ....
Shall we start by looking at the penguins ....

Now try these

Add the missing **apostrophes** to this passage.

"Were hungry, can we have our lunch?" David asked.
"Yes, its time to stop," Mrs Griffiths replied.
"I loved seeing the lions cubs, she was such a lovely mother," Jodie called.
"I agree but theyll soon grow!" giggled Amil.
"I want to see the giant tortoises pen next," said Helen.
"Okay, eat your lunch quickly and well have time," said Mrs Griffiths.

Challenge

This passage doesn't make sense.
Copy this passage adding the missing punctuation.

its time to go home class 3 climbed upon the coach feeling
happy but tired looking forward to getting back home for tea
my favourite animals were the wolves said gary
mine too exclaimed tom

....

....

....

....

Answers

LA = Learn About NTT = Now Try These C = Challenge

Pages 4–5

LA

- It is the beginning of the holidays.
- We are going to the seaside.
- I can't wait to build a sandcastle.

NTT *e.g.*

- Take a bucket and spade to the beach.
- Will the sea be really cold?

C

- We arrived at the beach very early in the morning. Mum and Dad wanted to get the best spot. We were having such fun that we didn't notice the tide coming in until our towels were all wet. Maybe Mum and Dad hadn't chosen the best spot after all.

LA

- Dad bought us an ice lolly each.
- She cried as her ice lolly melted.
- At last Holly was smiling again.

NTT *e.g.*

- It made us happy.
- Holly dropped hers on the sand.
- Dad went and bought her another one.

C

- A dog knocked over our sandcastle.
- Ben caught a jellyfish in a rock pool.
- We buried Dad in the sand.
- We walked home.

Pages 6-7

LA

- The sun was shining as I woke this morning.
- It is time I had my breakfast.

C

- Mr James Jackman
Sunnymead House, 32 Charlton Road
Edinburgh, Scotland, EL24 9DR

LA

- I love the book Charlotte's Web.
- Can we see Cinderella at the cinema?

NTT

- Monday, July, Christmas, Friday, September, May, Diwali, October

C

- Dear Ali,
We are having a great time in Australia. On Tuesday we went to the beach. On Friday we are going to the Sydney Opera House to see Joseph's Dreamcoat. Jake is scared by the spiders. I am being brave!

Pages 8-9

LA

- What is the time?
- Let's go and play.
- Where are my pyjamas?
- Why is it raining?

NTT

- what, when, who, where, which

C *e.g.*

- Does it have four legs?
- What colour is its fur?
- Where does it live?
- Would you keep it as a pet?

LA

- Why do I have to tidy my room?
- What shall I wear today?

NTT *e.g.*

- What did you make?
- Where are the two cartons of milk?
- Which flavour milkshake did you make?

C

- "Why do I have to go shopping?"
Kyle asked, "Can't I go to Sam's house instead?"
His mum replied, "I'm afraid not as Sam's Mum has to go shopping as well."
"Would you like to meet them for a pizza later?"
"Yes, can we?" said Kyle excitedly.

Pages 10-11

LA

- Can I smell smoke?
- Look at that fire!
- Quick, grab some water!
- Who started the fire?

NTT

surprise	anger	joy	pain
What a surprise!	Don't ever do that again!	I love it!	Ouch!
I don't believe it!	How dare you!	What great news!	That hurts!

C *e.g.*

- Look at the fire!
- Stay back, it's dangerous!

LA

- Watch out, the bath will overflow!
- I think you are wasting water!

NTT *e.g.*

- Look out!
- I can't wait!
- Hello!

C

Dear Ben,
We are having a great time! Yesterday we had a fire on the beach. It was brilliant! Then it rained. When you visit we will build a fire with you too. Love Kyle

Pages 12-13

LA

- The shopkeeper stacked tomatoes, cucumbers, onions and radishes.
- Mum bought kebabs, steaks and burgers for the BBQ.

NTT *e.g.*

- At the shoe shop they sell trainers, wellingtons and slippers.
- At the cake shop we saw bread, tarts and buns.
- The newsagent sells comics, newspapers and sweets.

C

- Hannah needs a pair of jeans, a purple T-shirt, two pairs of socks and new shoes.
- We need some dog food, a dog lead, a few toys and a bed for our new puppy.
- I could eat a bag of crisps, some pizza slices and a chocolate bar for a snack!

LA

- The scruffy, long-haired, muddy dog stole sweets from the shop.
- The shopkeeper screamed, yelled, ran and pounced on the dog.

NTT

- On Friday Mum took me shopping for a pair of shiny, new, blue shoes. In the first shoe shop we were greeted by a grumpy, tired assistant who prodded, yanked and squeezed my feet until they hurt. We left

Answers

that shop as soon as we could. The next shop sold boots, flip-flops, trainers and slippers but no shoes. Finally we bought some shoes. I came home with a pair of shiny, new, red shoes!

C *e.g.*
- At the zoo we saw lions, tigers, giraffes and penguins.
- I thought the giraffes were tall, graceful, elegant and beautiful.
- The lions were relaxing, yawning and washing themselves.

Pages 14-15

LA *e.g.*
- "Head it into the goal Dan!"
- Dan
- "Careful! Watch out for my greenhouse."

NTT *e.g.*
- Now look what you've done!
- We're really sorry.

C
- "I love having a picnic," said Bola.
- "Me too," replied Aimee.
- "We should eat quickly as I think it might rain!" muttered Ellie.

LA *The following sentences are correct.*
- "Grandad, can we go to the Water Park tomorrow?" asked Helen. ✓
- "What a good idea," muttered Grandad. ✓

NTT *e.g.*
- I'm looking forward to our trip.
- We can't go now, the car has a flat tyre.
- This is just as nice as the Water Park, Grandad.

C
- "I'm looking forward to our trip," said Helen.
- "We can't go now, the car has a flat tyre," said Grandad sadly.
- "This is just as nice as the Water Park, Grandad," said Helen.

Pages 16-17

LA
- Barney, our little black dog, watched the kittens from his bed.
- Then, to Barney's surprise, they started to eat his food!

NTT
- Our cat Tilly, who loves catching mice, usually brings them into the house.
- Cleo, an old cat, spends most of the day asleep on the sofa.
- George, a stray cat, often eats left-over food from restaurants.

LA
- The lions pounced on their prey, killing the antelope quickly.
- The lions relax in the shade of a tree, flies buzzing around them.

NTT
- The Golding Family were going on a day safari. They excitedly packed their camera and binoculars, at the last minute remembering the suncream. They were going to an animal watering hole, an uncomfortable and slow ride away on an unmade road. Eventually they got there, tired and sore. Suddenly their discomfort was forgotten, as a cheetah and her cub slowly wandered to the water for a drink. Before long a group of lions had joined them, the young ones playing at the water's edge. On the return journey, while bouncing in the back of the truck, the Golding Family talked about their exciting day.

C *e.g.*
- I climbed slowly into bed, exhausted but happy.
- The class ran into the playground, everyone shouting and laughing.
- The holidays finally started, after months of waiting.

Pages 18-19

LA
- do not = don't
- was not = wasn't
- could not = couldn't
- is not = isn't

NTT
- **haven't** = have not
- **they're** = they are
- **I'll** = I will
- **they'll** = they will
- **I've** = I have
- **she'll** = she will

C
- didn't = did not
- he'll = he will
- they've = they have
- we've = we have
- we're = we are
- you're = you are

LA
- (we) have = we've
- (she) will = she'll
- (we) will = we'll
- (they) are = they're
- (he) is = he's
- (I) have = I've

NTT
- **I would** = I'd
- **will not** = won't
- **of the clock** = o'clock
- **I had** = I'd
- **shall not** = shan't

C
- '**It's** time you had your hair cut!'
- 'But **it's** always been like this and you haven't worried.'
- 'True, but now a spider has made **its** home in your hair.'
- 'Ahhh, **it's** not true!'

Pages 20-21

LA
- Paragraph 2 Roald was
- Paragraph 3 When Roald
- Paragraph 4 By the
- Paragraph 5 He was

NTT *e.g.*
- Paragraph 2: Roald as a baby and his first introduction to exciting stories.
- Paragraph 3: Sad events that upset Roald as a young child.
- Paragraph 4: Roald's character age six.
- Paragraph 5: An event in Roald's young life.

C
- Roald's early life was full of interesting events. Some of them were sad, some were exciting. They all influenced him as he grew up.

Pages 22-23

LA
- "Let's go down to the river today," said Ben.
- "Good idea, we could take a picnic," replied Aziz.
- "I'll meet you in half an hour," called Ben as he dashed off to get ready.

Answers

NTT
- "Look at the boat," said Ben.
- "He's waving to us," giggled Aziz.
- "I think he needs help," said Ben, concerned.

C e.g.
- "That man needs help," said Ben.
- "I'll call for help," replied Aziz.

LA
- "I think we should call the fire brigade," replied Ben.
- "Look, there's a rope," said Aziz. "Shall we try and throw it to him?"

NTT
- "Can you catch this rope?" called Aziz.
- "Try again, I missed it," shouted the man.
- "OK, let's try one more time," said Ben.
- "I've caught it at last," laughed the man.

C
- "Hang on a minute while we tie the rope to this tree," called the boys.
- "Can you pull yourself in now?" Ben shouted.
- "Yes I can," the man replied. "Thank you so much."

Pages 24-25

LA
- Shall we play football. ✗
- I want to read quietly. ✓
- Let's make two mixed teams! ✗
- Can I play too? ✓
- Great goal! ✓
- Fantastic. ✗

NTT
- Shall we play football**?**
- Let's make two mixed teams**.**
- Fantastic**!**

C e.g.
- My friends and I played an exciting game of football.
- In the playground I invented a new game to play with the whole class.
- When will playtime start?
- Will it be sunny or raining at playtime?

LA
- Shall we play tag at playtime?
- I'll ask Nathan and Fran to play too.
- Quick, hurry up!
- That's a good idea.
- That's the bell, time for playtime.
- Where are the others?

NTT *e.g.*
- There are seven children in the playground.
- Is Charlie going to fall off the climbing frame?
- Look out William!

C

Mrs Singh asked her class if they would like an extra playtime**.** "Yes**!**" they all cheered. "It is a reward for the excellent work you have done this afternoon," she explained. "How about 10 minutes on the field**?**" The class ran out chatting and calling to each other**.**
- *e.g.* Six boys formed a football team.
- "Can I play?" asked Joe.
- "Sure!" replied Hamid.

Pages 26-27

LA
- the dog's bowl
- the man's jumper
- the child's homework
- Queen Elizabeth's crown
- the bird's nest
- the lion's tail

NTT
- Niall tore the book's page by accident.
- We were driving along when the car's tyre suddenly went flat.
- The plant's flower drooped in the sun.
- Mrs Thompson's cat was rushed to the vet after having an accident.

C e.g.
- This is my brother's coat.
- There is a thorn in my dog's paw.
- I love going to my auntie's house.

LA
- the players**'** shirts
- the dancers**'** shoes
- the swans**'** nests
- the shops**'** sales
- the girls**'** hats
- the lorries**'** drivers

NTT
- The doctors**'** surgeries
- The birds**'** nests
- The dogs**'** paws
- The gardeners**'** flowers

C
- The wind and rain plucked the roses**'** (or rose**'s**) petals from the bush.
- Lord Buckley**'s** horse sprinted across the field.
- The crows**'** (or crow**'s**) squawking woke the campers early in the morning.
- Many singers**'** voices could be heard as the music began.

Pages 28-29

LA
- **T**uesday, **M**rs **G**riffiths, **J**une

NTT
- I must remember my packed lunch, a coat in case it rains, some money and a pen.
- Class 3**,** the noisiest class in the school**,** waited impatiently for the coach.
- At last the coach**,** a big and smart one**,** arrived and we set off.

C e.g.
- "Do you think there will be lions there?" asked Julie.

"I hope so, I love lions," said Andrew.

"I like rhinos too!" added Julie.

LA
- The class arrived at the wildlife park and gathered around their teacher**.**
- At last we are here**!**
- Wow, look over there**!**
- Is it a tiger or a leopard**?**
- Class 3 was split into three groups and given clipboards**.**
- Shall we start by looking at the penguins**?**

NTT
- "We're hungry, can we have our lunch?" David asked.
- "Yes, it's time to stop," Mrs Griffiths replied.
- "I loved seeing the lion's cubs, she was such a lovely mother," Jodie called.
- "I agree but they'll soon grow!" giggled Amil.
- "I want to see the giant tortoises' pen next," said Helen.
- "Okay, eat your lunch quickly and we'll have time," said Mrs Griffiths.

C

It's time to go home. **C**lass 3 climbed upon the coach feeling happy but tired, looking forward to getting back home for tea.

"My favourite animals were the wolves,**"** said **G**ary.

"Mine too!**"** exclaimed **T**om.